CONTENTS

the**people**

the**moves**

the**talk**

JONATHAN NOLTE

Radar expert and BMX hotshot Jonathan Nolte has been freestyle riding for 17 years. Radar interviews Jonathan to find out what freestyle BMX is all about...

What is freestyle BMX?

BMX stands for bicycle motocross. It began as a racing sport on dirt tracks, but has grown to include amazingly creative riding (or freestyle) on a variety of surfaces. Freestyle BMX riders use small, simple bikes to jump and perform a range of impressive tricks and stunts.

How did you get into freestyle BMX?

I'd always been interested in pulling stunts on my bike and I began building small dirt jumps in the woods when I was a kid. One day my neighbours cleaned out their garage and threw out two BMX bikes. I put together a single working bike out of the two old ones, and began to teach myself flatland moves.

Tell us about flatland moves. What are they?

Basically, they are the moves you do on flat terrain. There are stacks of different ways of moving, such as spinning, rolling and balancing on one wheel. Then there's an endless list of cool trick names to learn!

What else can you get up to on a BMX?

Trail riding (also called 'dirt jumping') is really cool. It's all about big spins, bike- and body-twisting moves and long, high jumps – really challenging stuff! Vert is awesome, too. A vert is a very tall, vertical ramp. Riders shoot out of the top of the ramp to catch big air, then perform amazing tricks on the bike in mid air.

freestyle
bmx

Isabel Thomas

Published in 2013 by Wayland

Copyright © Wayland 2013

Wayland
Hachette Children's Books
338 Euston Road
London NW1 3BH

Wayland Australia
Level 17/207 Kent Street
Sydney NSW 2000

All rights reserved

Concept by Joyce Bentley

Commissioned by Debbie Foy and Rasha Elsaeed

Produced for Wayland by Calcium
Designer: Paul Myerscough
Editor: Sarah Eason

Photographer: Adam Lawrence

British Library Cataloguing in Publication Data

Thomas, Isabel, 1980–
    Freestyle BMX. — (Street sports)(Radar)
    1. Bicycle motocross—Juvenile literature.
    2. Stunt cycling—Juvenile literature.
    3. BMX bikes—Juvenile literature.
    I. Title II. Series
    796.6-dc22

ISBN: 978 0 7502 7787 7

Every effort has been made to clear copyright. Should there be any inadvertent omission, please apply to the publisher for rectification.

Printed in China

Wayland is a division of Hachette Children's Books, an Hachette UK company.

www.hachette.co.uk

Acknowledgements: Alamy: Keith Morris 30cl; Flickr: GeishaBoy500 1, 6r, Jon Hanson cover, 6bl, 7br, 26, Djenan Kozic 2–3, 31tl, Sabbath Photography 30bl, Talking Dog Photo 31tl; Getty Images: 8; Sarah Lari: 2t, 18bl, 19br; Jonathan Nolte: 3l, 5; PA Photos: 20; Raleigh UK: 24tc, 24c, 24–25b; Shutterstock: Haslam Photography 13, 21, Nito 25cl, Qik 2c, 28–29; Jonathan Zizzo: 18tl.

cover stories

Have you got a favourite BMX style?

Street is my favourite way to ride. It includes anything done on the streets where a rider lives or bikes. Riders use steps, ledges, cement banks, ditches, earth mounds, handrails, and anything else they can jump off, onto or over. I love it because the whole world becomes a giant BMX playground!

What do you need to look out for when starting to ride BMX?

Freestyle BMX can be dangerous, especially for beginners. Make sure you have the right protective gear, including a well-fitting helmet, and start off on small ramps in a skate park. Your ideal introduction would be to take a few starter lessons.

THE MOVES

manual

tailwhip air

one-footer air

Extreme stunts and big air make freestyle BMX a thrilling, high-adrenalin sport. Bikers use the urban landscape to invent exciting new moves, or they take advantage of specially built ramps to perform breathtaking tricks.

TAILWHIP AIR

During this vert move, the biker uses a ramp to gain air, then flicks the back end of the bike so it makes a full rotation around the forks.

MANUAL

To perform this flatland move, the biker pulls a wheelie, but without pedalling. If the biker gains enough momentum before going into the wheelie, the manual can be held for an impressive distance!

ONE-FOOTER AIR

A one-footer is a move in which only one foot is placed on a pedal. When this move is performed mid-jump, it is called a one-footer air.

HANG FIVE

To pull a hang five the biker lifts the tail end of the bike and holds his body weight forward. This flatland move is similar to a manual, but performed on the front wheel.

TUCK NO-HANDER

To perform this move the biker takes off from a ramp to get air, and tucks the handlebars between his legs. The biker then extends his arms so that he appears to be flying!

hang five

tuck no-hander

DAVE MIRRA

BMX SUPERSTAR!

THE STATS

Name: Dave Mirra
Born: 4 April 1974
Place of birth:
New York, USA
Personal life: Married
with children
Job: Professional
freestyle BMX rider

BMX KID

Dave started riding BMX when he was just four years old. Soon he was using home-made ramps to learn basic jumps and tricks. He won his first competition when he was just ten years old and by the age of 13 he was starting to get a name as an excellent rider.

SUPERSTAR RIDER

Dave turned pro at the age of 18 and soon became the master of BMX vert riding. The following year, disaster struck when Dave was hit by a car as he crossed the street, badly injuring his head and shoulder. Although doctors told him that he may never ride again, Dave never gave up on BMX riding.

THE CHAMP!

In 1996, just three years after his accident, the so-called 'Miracle Boy' won his first X Games gold medal and today he holds the X Games record for the most medals ever won, including 14 golds. He has created lots of freestyle BMX moves and in 2000 Dave became the first rider ever to do a double backflip in competition!

BIG BUSINESS

When it comes to BMX, Dave means business. He has his own video game, *Dave Mirra Freestyle BMX*, and his bike company produces state-of-the-art bikes specially designed for the different forms of BMX. The 'Miracle Boy' has proved that BMX is more than just a sport to him – it's a way of life.

Career highlights

1992 turned pro

1997 won double X Games gold

1998 launched own brand of bubble gum and breakfast cereal

2009 made X Games history by winning medals in every competition since they started

THE BUNNY HOP

This basic BMX flatland trick involves the rider lifting the front wheel off the ground, followed by the back wheel. This makes the bike 'hop' like a bunny!

You will need:

• BMX bike • helmet • elbow pads
• knee pads • fully pumped-up tyres

1

Stand on the pedals, bend your knees and elbows, and lean forward. Tense your whole body.

2

Pull back on the handlebars hard and fast to lift the bike off the ground.

3 Push the handlebars forward as your front wheel lifts off the ground. This lifts the rear wheel.

Got it?

Your bike should have popped off the ground and into the air. The more you practise this move, the bigger your hops will become. Once you have mastered the basic move, you can add a mid-air spin to perform a 180° bunny hop (see pages 16–17).

4 Straighten your legs as the rear wheel falls back towards the ground. Then loosen your arms and allow the front wheel to drop. Bend your knees on landing to take the impact.

Type 'BMX bunny hop' into www.youtube.com to see this move in action.

FREESTYLE SPEAK

Boost up your BMX lingo
with the rad Radar guide!

180
a move in which the rider
does a 180° turn by spinning
the bike in a half circle

360
a move in which the rider
does a 360° turn by spinning
the bike in one full circle

air/big air
any gap between the
tyres and the ground

boost
to ride a BMX bike as fast
as possible in order to get
maximum air before jumping
off a ramp

box jump
a double-sided ramp with a
flat platform on top

dialled
when a bike is set up so that
everything works perfectly
and suits the rider

dirt riding
a style of freestyle BMX
that takes place on rough
terrain such as woodland

flatland
a style of freestyle BMX
riding that does not involve
obstacles. In flatland,
tricks are performed
on a level surface

foam pit
a pit that is filled with foam
that riders land in while
practising jumps

grind
sliding the bike along a
surface, such as a ledge

gyrator spin
a spin of 360°

half-pipe
a U-shaped ramp used by
BMX riders

jam
getting together with
other BMX riders for a
biking session

lip trick
a trick performed on the edge
of a ramp or vert by stopping
the bike with at least one
wheel on the platform

mash
to push down hard on
the pedals to make the
bike go faster

quarter-pipe
a curved ramp that is
one half of a half-pipe

rad
amazing, cool

shredded
to perform a move well

stall
when a rider lands the bike
on an edge or ramp, and
pauses before continuing
with his routine

stoppie
to slam on the brakes
or jam a foot in the front
spokes to lift the bike's
back wheel

superman

a move in which the biker kicks out his legs so that the body is horizontal – as though he is flying!

vert riding

a style of riding that takes place on the vert and often involves amazing aerial tricks

wheelie hop

a trick in which the biker performs a wheelie while 'hopping' on the back wheel

vert

a tall, vertical ramp used by BMX riders

wheelie

a trick in which the biker lifts the front wheel off the ground

GLOSSARY

adrenalin

a hormone found in the human body that causes the heart to beat faster

condo

short for condominium – a property in a block of apartments

coping

the edge of a structure such as a quarter-pipe

customise

to change something so that it suits your needs

erode

to wear away

freestyle

having no rules or regulations

instinctive

a response to something or urge to do something that does not require thought – a gut reaction

momentum

an impelling force or strength of movement

motocross

a form of motorcycle racing on rough terrain in which bikers compete against each other on specially adapted motorbikes

terrain

a term used to describe a type of land, for example 'rocky terrain'

urban landscape

the structure and shape of a city

X Games

an extreme sports competition held every year in LA, USA

FREE RIDER

MITCH GREEN'S STORY

When I was a kid, I used to play ice hockey and to train for it I would rollerblade at a local skate park. By the age of 16, I was getting tired of the ice hockey scene, so when I saw the BMX bikers at the skate park, I knew I just had to give it a go!

A friend was into freestyle BMX, so he helped me to buy my first bike and learn the moves. Next, I set myself a goal: to learn to freestyle BMX in six months! Luckily, I quickly picked up the basic moves and before long I was pulling some really rad stunts. Then I found an indoor skate park nearby that had amazing ramps and obstacles and I started riding there. Soon, I started building my own bike.

One day, I went down to practise at the local skate park and saw that a competition was taking place. I'd only been riding for about eight months, but when I was asked to join in I decided to give it a shot. I pulled some decent stunts and won a pair of Roadstar handlebars! It was a real buzz and it inspired me to try out some more challenging tricks after that. Once you start, you don't want to stop!

Even though I've only been riding for two years, I have a full-time job at the indoor skate park where I teach beginners. I love riding and I'm determined to make a career of it – there is nothing like BMX.
I hope to get a sponsorship deal soon – then I know I'll have really made it.

THE DISASTER

The disaster is a basic trick to master once you can ride the ramps and do a bunny hop with a 180° turn (see pages 10–11). It involves riding at a steady speed so that you maintain control of the bike throughout the stunt.

You will need:

• BMX bike • helmet
• elbow pads • knee pads
• fully pumped-up tyres

1

Ride up the ramp and pull up your handlebars to bunny hop.

2

Turn your bike 180° while it is in the air.

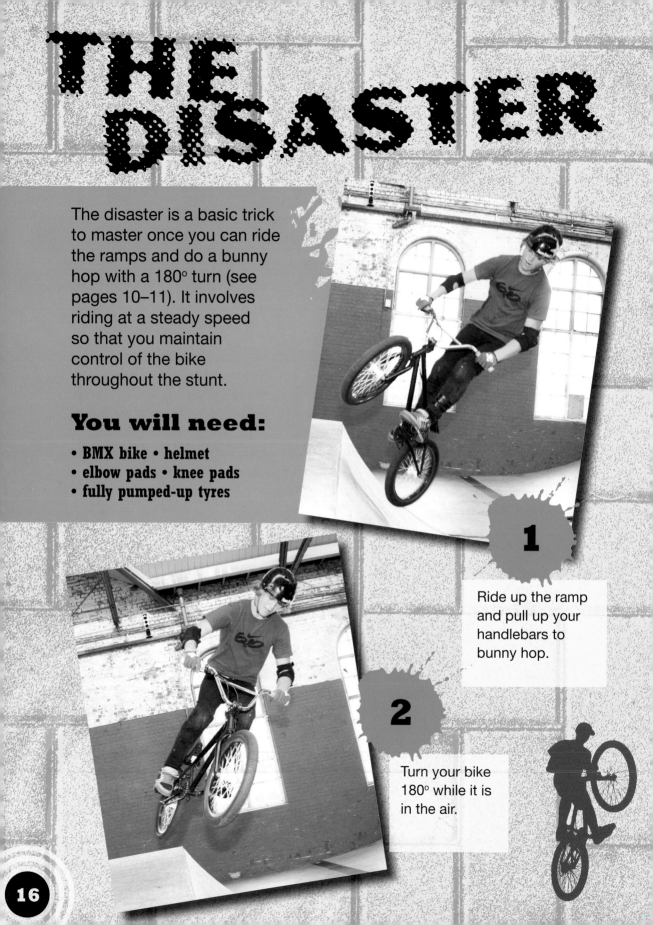

3

Land your
back wheel
on the ramp.

4

Stall, then lift your
back wheel over the
coping and ride off!

Got it?

If you rode up the ramp,
turned and stalled with
your back wheel on the
platform before riding back
down, then you've mastered
a disaster! Now build on this
move to learn new and more
challenging ramp tricks.

A WEEK IN THE LIFE OF PRO BMX RIDER

CODY HENNINGS

blog   **news**   **events**

MONDAY

I headed to the skate park this morning to give a BMX lesson. Everything was going great until I snapped a brake cable. After a quick fix at the bike shop, I ran into another kid I teach and ended up giving a second lesson. That was my day — but I love it!

TUESDAY

There were no shows or events today, so I went to the skate park just to ride. I shredded some new vert tricks in the afternoon, then my boss and I loaded up the trailer for our team's BMX show tomorrow.

WEDNESDAY

Today was a 6.00am start. We had a three-hour drive to our freestyle show at a high school in Copperas Cove, Texas. Road trips are awesome. When we arrived, we set up a box jump and did some cool lip tricks.

blog news events

THURSDAY

We started the day by setting up ramps for our shows at the State Fair of Texas. Then it was back to the condo we're staying in for a team meeting. We're feeling totally pumped for tomorrow. Bring it on!

FRIDAY

Today was the opening day at the State Fair. I worked on my bike and made sure everything was dialled in, then rode the ramps to get warmed up. Then it was show time! We pulled a big crowd and they seemed pretty impressed by our vert moves. Then we chilled until the next show.

SATURDAY

Our second day at the fair, and today was our freestyle show. It was pretty windy when we got there but it didn't stop us throwing down the 360s and totally nailing a superman!

THE FREESTYLE BMX STORY

When adventurous cyclists began racing over the crazy bumps and jumps of motocross tracks, bicycle motocross (BMX) was born. Riders did tricks between races to have fun and impress their friends. Some began to enjoy the stunts more than the racing.

Bob Haro wowed audiences with his impressive freestyle stunts at BMX shows during the 1980s.

SWIMMING POOLS TO SKATE PARKS

Inspired by skateboarding, early BMX riders practised stunts in empty swimming pools or on backyard ramps. When skate parks appeared in the 1970s, BMXers used the skateboarders' ramps and verts to do amazing tricks. By the end of the decade, skate parks were holding adrenalin-fuelled sessions just for BMX riders.

FREESTYLING

In 1980, BMX riders Bob Haro and R.L. Osborn formed the BMX Action Trick Team, a touring squad of freestyle BMXers. Photos and videos of their stunts and tricks caught on and in the early 1980s, the world went BMX crazy. *Freestylin'* magazine was launched in 1984, and bike manufacturers began building bikes customised to suit freestyle BMX.

From street to stadium

THE FLAIR

The flair is a white-knuckle ramp trick in which the biker performs a somersault in mid air. This move should be attempted only by very experienced riders!

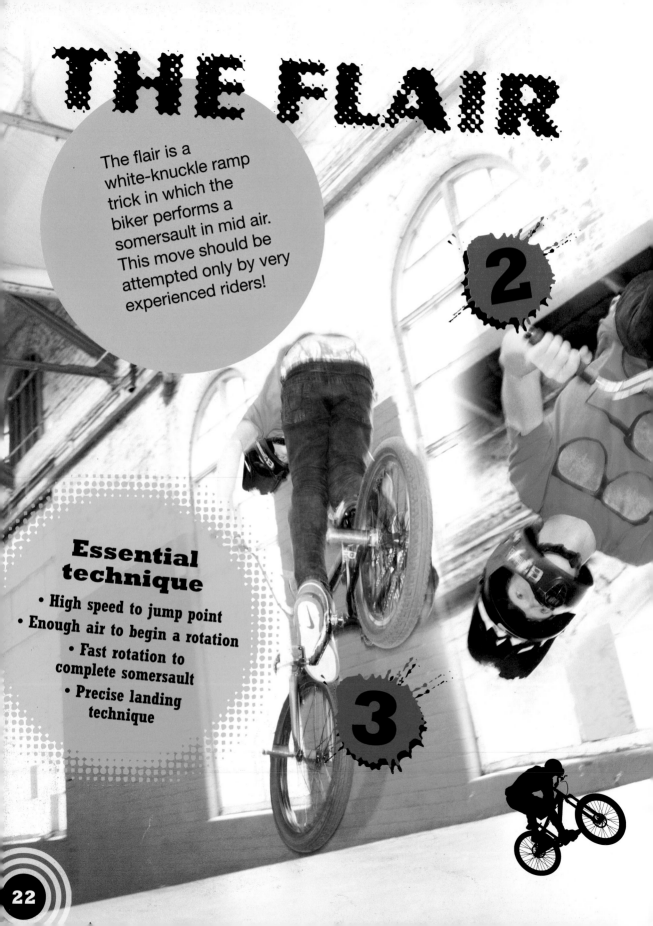

2

3

Essential technique

- High speed to jump point
- Enough air to begin a rotation
- Fast rotation to complete somersault
- Precise landing technique

1

HOW IT'S DONE

1. The biker rides hard at the ramp to make sure he has enough speed, and giving him plenty of momentum.

2. The biker boosts out of the ramp, throwing his weight backwards and turning himself and the bike over into a backflip.

3. The biker continues to rotate through the backflip until he is upright again and ready to land on the downward ramp.

WHY DO IT?

The flair looks awesome and can be combined with other tricks to make it look even more impressive. Professional freestyle BMX bikers often try to outdo each other on the height or number of rotations – a double rotation gets the top score!

BMX KIT

skateboard-style helmet must be worn for safety

Smaller and stronger than road bikes, freestyle BMX bikes are designed for pulling impressive stunts and tricks. Beginners can buy a ready-made BMX bike and customise it with different parts as they improve. Many experienced riders build their own bikes from scratch!

gloves prevent blisters and help sweaty hands to grip the handlebars

BASIC BIKES

A typical freestyle bike has a strong steel-alloy frame and parts that do not easily bend out of shape. A small saddle maximises legroom. Pegs can be screwed to the wheel axles and used for tricks such as grinds and stalls.

The basic BMX bike can be customised for different BMX styles.

seat

rear brake

cranks

spokes

VERT AND DIRT

Bikes customised for riding ramps have extra-strong frames. Vert bikes are heavier than other BMX bikes – they are built for maximum strength so they do not shatter on impact when landing big jumps. Dirt bikes are designed to fly in dirt track racing! They have grooved tyres for gripping dirt tracks, and lightweight, but sturdy, frames for jumping.

brake lever

brake cables

frame

hard knee pads are often worn under loose trousers

front brake

peg

fork

Bikers use pegs to 'hook' the bike onto a ledge during a trick or they stand on them for stability when performing a stunt.

pedals

FLATLAND AND STREET

Flatland and street bike tyres are thick and smooth to grip concrete. Short frames allow the rider to climb around the bike easily. A mechanism lets the handlebars turn through 360° without tangling the brake cables.

20-inch wheel

tyre

THE VERT

You are almost at the end of your run and your stomach is in knots. It's time to pull your biggest air yet. You have landed it in the foam pit, but now you are facing a 10-metre fall onto a hard ramp. Your heart is pounding like a drum and inside your gloves your hands feel damp and clammy on your handlebars. You squeeze the grips tighter.

RAMP IT UP

You mash down on the pedals to build speed, focusing on the moves ahead. The crowd cheers. A surge of pure adrenalin rushes through your body. Game on!

THE ZONE

You swoop up the half-pipe and boost out of the ramp. You are flying like a bird. You have reached the 'zone': you don't think, you just *do*. Your body twists and turns automatically. Everything around you is a kaleidoscope of spinning shapes and colours.

LANDING

The air rushes past your face as you fall. Your eyes lock on the ramp, looking for re-entry. You land it perfectly and before you know it, you are rolling across flat ground. A smile breaks out on your face. It is the best stunt you have ever pulled. The crowd goes wild, but you barely hear the applause. You just want to keep riding.

What's the buzz?

BMX riders experience a state of mind while riding called the 'zone'. This is when riding the bike becomes completely instinctive.

SUPER STUNTS!

Only a freestyler could drop from the height of a six-storey building and roll away without a scratch. Check out this and other record-breaking BMX moves…

WICKED WHEELIE!

Who: Stephane Colley
When: 1984
Where: France
What: Longest wheelie
How: Pedalled 36 kilometres around a stadium track in two hours and 29 minutes!

AWESOME AIR!

Who: Kevin Robinson
When: 2008
Where: Central Park, New York, USA
What: Highest air
How: Boosted 8.23 metres above a quarter-pipe airing 16.46 metres off the ground. This is the same height as a six-storey building!

SPINS PER MIN!

Who: Takahiro Ikeda
When: 2011
Where: Japan
What: Most gyrator (360°) spins
How: Completed 59 gyrator spins in one minute!

HOPPING MAD!

Who: Manual Torres
When: 2009
Where: X Games, LA, USA
What: Most wheelie hops
How: Performed 62 wheelie hops in 30 seconds

BUNNY BUSINESS!

Who: Bryan Ventura
When: 2009
Where: X Games, LA, USA
What: Most bunny hops
How: Managed an awesome 41 bunny hops in 30 seconds – more than one per second!

SUPER STOPPIES!

Who: Travis Frohlich
When: 2010
Where: X Games, LA, USA
What: Record number of stoppies
How: Racked up 115 stoppies

ONE-MINUTE WHEELIES!

Who: Guadalupe Alvarez
When: 2010
Where: X Games, LA, USA
What: Most wheelies
How: Set a new world record for 167 wheelies per minute

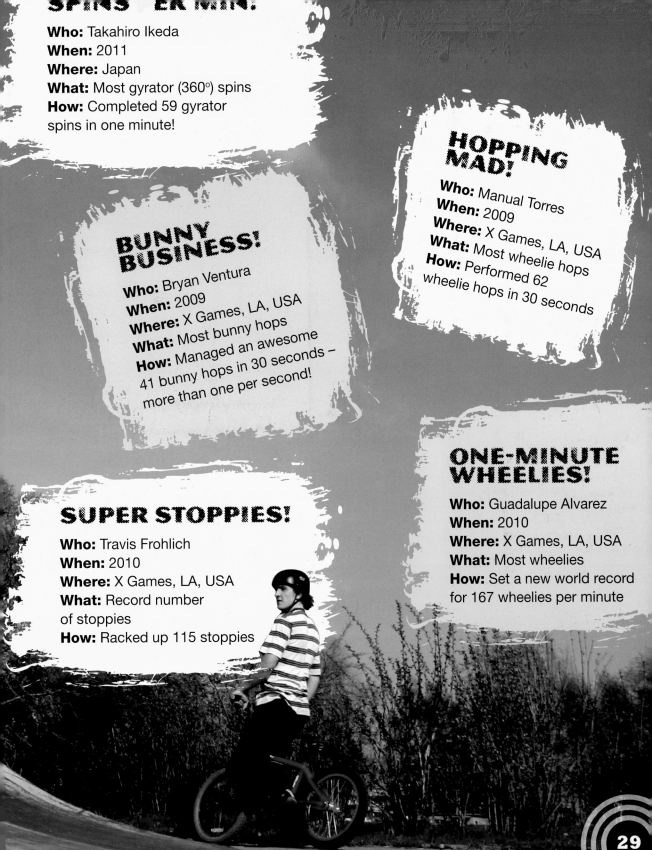

RAD OR BAD?

FOR?

Fans of the sport argue that freestyle BMX is a creative and thrilling sport with many positives attached to it. They say that:

1. Freestyle BMX helps kids to increase their personal fitness levels and provides a great cardio-vascular workout while having fun.
2. It is a great way to channel energy and offers a cool subculture to hook into, which includes music, fashion and lifestyle.
3. Freestyle BMX can be carried out on all kinds of terrain – from parks, woods and countryside to streets and urban skate parks.
4. Many of the tricks and stunts are challenging and so they encourage kids to work hard to achieve their goals.
5. Biking, whether to get around or as a hobby, is environmentally sound and is likely to produce competent cyclists for the future.
6. Many freestyle BMXers build and customise their own bikes, which develops excellent mechanical skills and encourages creative expression.
7. If freestyle BMX becomes an Olympic sport then it will be regarded with the same respect as any other cycling sport.

AGAINST

However, some people think that freestyle BMX is a dangerous and antisocial sport with many negative points. They say that:

1. Unlike other street sports such as free running or street football, BMX can be an expensive sport for a beginner to get started in. Peer pressure to upgrade to the latest bike or gear may also occur.
2. BMX jams are considered antisocial and noisy events that can appear threatening to local residents or pedestrians.
3. As an extreme sport, freestyle BMX can be dangerous or fatal if the rider fails to wear the correct safety gear.
4. Some dirt riders do not respect the countryside. They leave litter and erode countryside trails.
5. Freestyle BMX riders need great upper body strength to perform stunts and so this can make it difficult for many girls to compete at a high level.

Rad or Bad?

Freestyle BMX is great way to get fit and have fun. As with any extreme sport, you need to protect yourself, other people and respect property. Indoor skate parks are a safe and supportive environment in which to practise the sport.

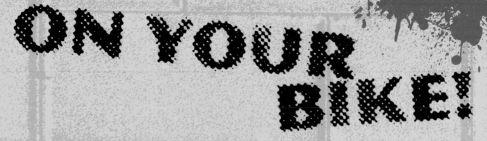

ON YOUR BIKE!

People to talk to

Wheelie your way into BMX – one of the most exciting extreme sports around. Radar can help to get you started and shredding your moves in no time!

To find out about BMX parks near you search:
www.extremesportsmap.com

British Bike Association
For information on skate parks, BMX biking and blogs check out:
www.bikes.org.uk

Watch the pros

Watch the pros in action at Relentless NASS, or join them on Facebook, MySpace or Bebo by clicking through:
www.relentlessnass.com

DVDs, Reads & Apps

Take a look at the awesome BMX mags available, such as *Ride BMX* or *BMX Plus,* to get the latest news, moves and reviews.

For another cool read, try:
BMX Riding Skills: The Guide to Flatland and Tricks by Shek Hon (Firefly Books, 2010)

Learn from the 'Miracle Boy' himself with *Dave Mirra's Trick Tips 1: BMX Basics* DVD

Boost into BMX-speak with the *BMX Dictionary* app:
www.itunes.com

INDEX